C000192854

THE MOLE

R. DAVID STONE

CONTENTS

Cover: *A patient observer may be rewarded with a rare glimpse of a mole suddenly popping out of a tunnel.*

Series editor: Jim Flegg.

Copyright © 1992 by R. David Stone. First published 1992.
Number 61 in the Shire Natural History series. ISBN 0 7478 0171 1.

British Library Cataloguing in Publication Data:
Stone, R. David.
The mole.
I. Title.
599.33.

Printed in Great Britain by C. I. Thomas & Sons (Haverfordwest) Ltd,
Press Buildings, Merlins Bridge, Haverfordwest, Dyfed SA61 1XF.

1. *Rarely seen on the surface, moles occasionally venture above ground in search of nesting materials.*

Introduction

To most people the merest mention of a mole conjures up one of two images: either that of a garment, such as a pair of traditional moleskin trousers or breeches; a waistcoat; or, more usually, a garden plot devastated by miniature volcano-shaped mounds of precious topsoil. Yet, despite the common, almost everyday observation of the latter phenomenon and the widespread distribution of 'the little gentleman in black velvet', few people have observed the living animal. Even those who have been fortunate enough to catch a mere glimpse of a mole will not have been able to glean much information about the animal, its lifestyle or its social behaviour. This is not surprising since, despite being one of Europe's most common small mammals, it is also one of the most secretive and hence intriguing.

Moles belong to the group of animals known as insectivores, which literally means 'insect-eaters'. While this is one of the few common traits of all members of this diverse group of animals (including the familiar hedgehogs and shrews), it is nonetheless a rather misleading term since these animals feed on a much wider range of prey items than insects. Moreover, many animals which are extremely specialised insect-feeders, for example the giant ant-eaters of South America or the bizarre scaly pangolins of Africa and Asia, all of which are toothless, are not included in this group.

Taxonomically, moles belong to the family Talpidae ('true moles'), which includes species such as the European mole (*Talpa europaea*), the extraordinary star-nosed moles (*Condylura cristata*) of North America, the shrew moles of Asia and the aquatic and highly endangered desmans of the Pyrenean mountain range and northern Iberia (*Galemys pyrenaicus*), as well as their cousins in western Russia (*Desmana moschata*). Golden moles — so called because of the glorious golden sheen of their fur — are found in many parts of southern Africa but, for scientific reasons, are classified under a different group, the family Chrysochloridae. Remarkably similar in appearance, but unrelated to the golden moles of Africa or the true moles of the northern hemisphere, is the Australian mar-

2

supial mole (*Notoryctes typhlops*), which is again classified in a separate family, the Notoryctidae. Almost nothing is known about this intriguing species, which lives in the hot deserts of Australia.

Moles of the family Talpidae are widely distributed throughout Eurasia and North America. These predominantly burrowing insectivores (29 species in twelve genera) are highly secretive and because of their fossorial lifestyle have been little studied. The single species which has received most attention from naturalists and biologists has been the common or European mole, whose lifestyle and behaviour are, in certain respects, representative of many of the other species.

This species is widely distributed throughout Europe and is particularly common in Great Britain. Although absent from Ireland, moles are found on a large number of islands off the coast of Britain, including Jersey, Alderney, Anglesey, Wight, Skye and Mull. There are no clear records as to how moles reached some of these islands: in some instances they would already have been present before the islands broke off from the mainland, whereas in others it is possible that they swam to these locations, aided by the currents and

2. *The skeletal (top) and muscular (lower) arrangement of the forelimbs of a mole.*

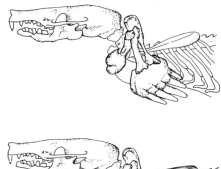

floating vegetation. It is also conceivable that moles were artificially introduced to certain areas, as has been witnessed for a range of other animals.

On continental Europe the same species is also the most commonly found mole and in much of western Europe it is the only species of mole. To the east and south of Switzerland and Italy, however, two other species are encountered: the blind mole (*Talpa caeca*) and the Roman mole (*Talpa romana*). Almost nothing is known about the behaviour or ecology of these species and, at first appearance, they are very difficult to tell apart.

PHYSICAL CHARACTERISTICS

Moles are highly specialised for a subterranean, digging way of life. Their broad, spade-like forelimbs, which have developed as powerful digging organs, are attached to muscular shoulders and a deep chestbone. The skin on the chest is thicker than elsewhere on the body as this region supports the most weight when the animal digs or sleeps. Behind the powerful shoulders, the body is almost cylindrical, tapering slightly to narrow hips, short sturdy limbs which are not especially adapted to digging — and a short, club-shaped tail, which is usually held erect. In most species, both pairs of limbs have an extra bone which increases the surface area of the paws, for support in the hindlimbs and for moving earth with the forelimbs.

The elongated head tapers to a hairless fleshy pink snout, which is highly sensory. In one species, the North American star-nosed mole, the development of this organ is taken to the extreme, bearing 22 mobile tentacles, each armed with thousands of sensory organs. These same organs are found in the pig-like nose of the common European mole and, being richly supplied with blood vessels, are highly sensitive to odours, changes in temperature and humidity. The nasal region is also endowed with a bunch of touch-sensitive vibrissae (bristles). Similar touch receptors are located on the tip of the tail, which is carried erect like an antenna, giving the animal a somewhat comical appearance, resembling a city tram connected to the overhead powerline.

External bodily appendages are reduced to a minimum amongst most mole species. For example, the ear pinnae are greatly reduced compared to those of other small mammals, and are usually difficult to locate. They consist of a circular opening, some 2 mm in diameter, which is fringed by short fine hairs and which leads to the inner ear structures. Moles utter both very low twittering sounds — especially between a female and her young — and high-pitched shrieks. The latter are usually evoked when the animal is being attacked or if it detects another animal in its tunnel system. In general, however, the auditory senses are not keenly developed in moles.

The eyes, too, are reduced in size and generally hidden behind the dense fur. In some species, for example the blind mole (*Talpa caeca*), which is found in northern Italy, the eyes are covered with a flap of skin, as in the African golden moles. In structure the eyes are perfectly formed, having all the features which are required for normal vision, although not all of these are highly developed. Thus it appears that, while moles are able to perceive certain features such as a light source, its intensity and even sudden movements nearby, they cannot focus rapidly on distant objects.

In carrying out their routine daily errands, moles probably rely on a combination of four senses: hearing, sight, touch and smell. Of these, the keen sense of smell seems to be the single most important modality for locating prey and also for detecting the presence of other animals. Prey is detected only at short range, but moles are able to detect water from far greater distances, often over 1 km. When active, a mole's snout is continuously moving, savouring the cocktail of odours which waft through the tunnel network on the air currents, or gathering information from a specific scent. Moles possess a wide range of scent glands, the most important of which transmit information about the owner's individual identity, its sex and reproductive condition. Secretions from these glands are now known to play a crucial role in the territorial behaviour of individual moles, which are able to distinguish between the odours of their long-standing neighbours, which they can recognise, and those of an intruding, unfamiliar animal, whose odour would not be recognised.

In addition to this formidable battery of sensory equipment, moles appear to have a keenly developed sense of orientation. This is believed to assist animals when constructing new, or repairing old, tunnels in that they retain a mental blueprint of the entire tunnel network. Certainly moles possess an acute awareness of the spatial arrangement of their own tunnel system.

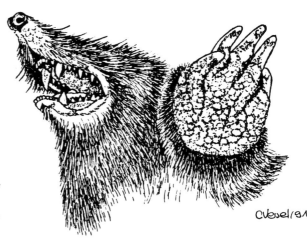

3. *The hairless, fleshy snout of a mole is highly sensitive to odours and touch, as well as to changes in temperature and humidity.*

4

4. *The farmer's peril: raised tunnels in a freshly tilled field indicate that a mole is in the process of establishing a new territory.*

The burrow

BURROW STRUCTURE

The mole's tunnel system is an elaborate, maze-like network of burrows, with no two animals creating a similar arrangement. The design, structure and overall dimensions of an individual's burrow system appear to be largely dictated by the quality of the habitat. For example, in shallow stony ground burrows may cover an extensive area but are usually arranged on just a single level. In contrast, in an area of old undisturbed pasture tunnels are more commonly multi-tiered, often with as many as six different levels of burrows superimposed upon each other.

When moles first colonise an area, each animal creates a series of shallow tunnels, 5-10 cm deep, which serve to provide protection and immediate prey rations. Moles create these tunnels by bracing their body against the tunnel floor and thrusting upwards and to the side with their forelimbs to displace and compress the soil. This is a slow process and, having dug a few strokes with one paw, the mole rotates its body through 180 degrees and digs with the other, thereby resting the muscles of each limb for short periods and also ensuring that the tunnel will be of equal and adequate diameter

throughout. These tunnels appear as slightly raised ridges on the surface and are often seen in freshly tilled fields.

A second and equally important function of these initial tunnels may be exploratory, in that it should be important for a new arrival to locate neighbouring moles at an early stage, since it is not wise to set up home in another mole's territory. Indeed this is the specific purpose of yet another type of temporary tunnel created during the breeding season, either by the already described technique of digging or, if the soil is sufficiently light in texture, by using both forelimbs simultaneously in a 'breast-stroke' swimming action. These tunnels have been aptly referred to as *traces d'amour*, or courtship runs, by some of the early French naturalists since, created only by males, they serve in the location of distant non-neighbouring breeding females with whom they will try to mate. Such tunnels are of limited use and duration and are generally used only once.

During these first crucial stages of colonisation, no proper nest is made, and the mole simply sleeps in either a small chamber that will have been constructed to the side of the tunnel, or else within the tunnel itself.

Once the groundwork has been laid and the preliminary series of tunnels created,

5. *The muscular forelimbs of a mole are broad, spade-like appendages with long, sharp claws for dislodging earth.*

moles then set about establishing a deeper, more permanent system of habitation. The digging techniques employed in the construction of these tunnels are quite different from those involved in creating shallow burrows, since this technique relies on the expulsion of earth from below ground. In this process, soil is loosened from the dig-ging face with the forelimbs and, with the same digging action, swept back along the sides, where it gathers in the tunnel behind the animal. (It was previously believed that moles also chiselled away earth with their teeth, but this is now known not to be so.) When an amount of soil has accumulated behind the mole it stops digging and turns

6. *Shallow tunnels are constructed in light soils by simply pushing the soil upwards with one paw, while simultaneously packing the floor of the tunnel with the other paw.*

C. Versel / 91

around by performing a somersault within the confines of the tunnel, to face the excavated earth. This is then pushed ahead of the mole along the newly dug tunnel until it reaches the point where a vertical shaft leading to the surface has already been dug. The soil is then pushed up this shaft by bracing the body against the tunnel wall and pushing the soil upwards to form the easily recognisable volcano-shaped spoil heaps or molehills. Thus it is the combination of strength and alternate pushing movements with the forepaws which expels this earth, and not a pushing motion of the head and neck region, as was originally believed. One of the behavioural differences between the 'true' moles of Europe and North America and their African relatives is the fact that the latter have very differently shaped forelimbs which chisel away at the earth face when digging tunnels, and it is the head and not the forelimbs which is used to move earth. For this reason, golden moles have a tough, leathery patch above the nose — with which they push the earth — and most species have completely concealed eyes.

It has been estimated that when excavating its burrow a mole may move more than 6 kg of soil in twenty minutes; comparing the weight of a large mole (100 grams) with that of an average human male (70 kg), this is equivalent to a man moving more than 4 tonnes of earth!

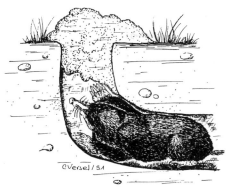

7. *The construction of deeper tunnels requires that the excavated earth is pushed out on to the surface, forming the familiar volcano-shaped molehills.*

A suitable habitat free from disturbances such as ploughing, flooding or eviction by another mole would most likely serve as home to an animal for its lifetime. The burrow is therefore a long-term investment which, once constructed, requires only maintenance of damaged tunnels on a daily basis, with some additional seasonal adjustments in response to climatic changes and fluctuations in the abundance of prey.

Moles display a keen sense of awareness, orientation and spatial memory, as displayed by some animals which may con-

8. *Although rarely venturing into water, moles are strong swimmers, which is crucial for those animals that live in low-lying areas prone to seasonal flooding.*

struct tunnels at the same place each year. Anybody who has attempted to catch moles will also verify that these animals are highly familiar with their tunnel systems, since any foreign object, such as a mole trap, placed in line with existing tunnels, will usually be filled up with earth! The resident mole invariably circumvents the obstacle, pausing long enough to get rid of unwanted soil, creating a new tunnel beneath or around the obstacle, to reconnect on the far side with the original tunnel. Likewise, during times of flooding, if forced out of their tunnels by the rising water level, moles seek refuge on higher ground such as railway embankments or hillsides. When the water level recedes, the moles return to reoccupy their original burrow systems.

Under such circumstances where tunnels may be prone to seasonal inundations, one may question why moles do not remain permanently on the surrounding higher ground. The most likely reason for this is that areas such as railway embankments are neither easy to dig in nor very high in prey concentrations, unlike the more fertile alluvial plains of river banks or valleys with their bountiful supply of invertebrates.

WHY CREATE A BURROW?

It is commonly believed that moles actively dig in search of food items. While this is certainly true of the African golden mole (*Erimitalpa granti*) and the marsupial mole (*Notoryctes typhlops*), which live in the sand dunes of the Namib Desert and the Australian outback respectively and cannot create permanent tunnels because of the continually shifting substratum, species such as the European mole have developed a more sophisticated means of obtaining prey. By constructing a semi-permanent series of tunnels, which may descend to over 1 metre within the soil column, moles obtain their daily rations by means of an elaborately laid trap. Many soil invertebrates such as earthworms, fly and beetle larvae show a distinct pattern of diurnal vertical movements through the soil, with many, for example earthworms, coming to the surface at sunset to feed and mate, only to retreat into the soil again as dawn approaches. In making such vertical daily movements, invertebrates invariably drop into the tunnels created by moles, where often, rather than digging their way through the tunnel walls again, they simply squirm along the extensive system of passages.

9. Cross-section of a breeding chamber and associated tunnel network. Earthworms that migrate through the soil column on a daily basis often fall into the tunnel, where they will be detected by the vigilant resident.

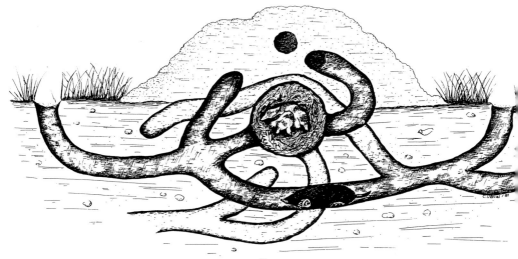

10 (above). *Moles come to the surface occasionally to collect nesting material and to disperse. They are very vulnerable to predation when out of their tunnels.*

11 (below left). *Close relative to the European mole, the Pyrenean desman is an endangered semi-aquatic animal found only in the French Pyrenees and northern Spain.*

12 (below right). *A rare view of the giant golden mole from South Africa.*

13. *The nest usually contains locally abundant materials, in this case grasses, which are woven into a spherical ball.*

Thus prey may be collected in a passive manner by the mole patrolling its tunnel system and gathering up the harvest. Even so, resident moles must still be vigilant lest neighbouring moles or even other small mammals such as woodmice breach the tunnel network in search of an easy meal.

THE NEST

Moles usually occupy just a single nest site, although during the breeding season females have been found to use up to three different nests, to which juveniles may be moved if the original nest is disturbed. The majority of a mole's resting time is spent at the nest, although each animal will occasionally take a short nap (ten to fifteen minutes) in the tunnel system without constructing any form of nest. This often occurs when excavating new tunnels.

The nest is usually located in a specially enlarged chamber, positioned to one side of a main tunnel and partially filled with nesting material. A permanent nest site always has a great number of tunnels leading to and from the chamber, providing a number of possible escape routes should the animal be threatened.

A wide variety of materials is used in nest construction, ranging from dry grasses, maize, oak and sycamore leaves to newspapers and lambs' wool. The mole gathers nesting material from the surface by coming partly out of a tunnel and grasping at nearby materials with its mouth. These are then carried to the nest chamber and, together with already existing materials, woven into a spherical ball. The principal fabric used for nest construction always reflects locally abundant matter so that, in woodlands for example, nests are almost entirely composed of leaves, while in pasture grasses will be used. One of the main functions of a nest is to provide insulation and to retain body heat when the mole is in the nest. In this respect, during the course of research, the author has found several mole nests that have been lined with pieces of plastic (potato-crisp and fertiliser bags),

10

which probably increased the insulating property of the nest!

One of the many unsolved mysteries of mole behaviour concerns the construction of large molehills or earth heaps which differ from the usual hills both in size (they often reach 1 metre in height) and in structure. These impressive heaps of earth, often having an internally intricate network of tunnels usually centred around a nest, have been termed 'fortresses'. Since these structures are most commonly found during the spring in areas prone to flooding, it was first believed that they were built by breeding females so that juveniles would avoid drowning. However, it is now apparent that this is not so since they are often built during the winter period, before breeding, and, in addition, are occasionally constructed by males. Indeed current investigations suggest an alternative hypothesis for the existence of these complex structures: in areas where soil cover is thin and in areas prone to fluctuating water levels, nests cannot be constructed at any great depth in the soil column. Therefore, because of their proximity to the surface, the nests are prone to major heat losses due to the lack of insulation. To compensate for this, nests are covered with large mounds of earth, which replicates the act of burying a nest within the soil column, thereby conserving heat. If this is so, then the fortress should be viewed as a monument to the moles' ingenuity and architectural prowess.

14. *A litter of juvenile star-nosed moles in the nest, before dispersal. Even at an early age, the most prominent features of the body are the broad forelimbs.*

15. *Similar in many respects to the European mole, the aptly named golden mole from Africa is blind, with some species living in sand dunes.*

16. *The Hottentot mole is adapted to living in dry regions and has short, chisel-like forelimbs for breaking through hard soil.*

17. *The European mole, widely distributed throughout Europe and particularly common in Great Britain.*

18. *Exquisitely arranged tentacles on the nose of a star-nosed mole, from the United States.*

Diet and feeding

All moles are insectivorous and, in most cases, specialists in hunting earthworms, their favourite prey. An adult mole requires up to 50 grams of food each day, or approximately half its body weight, to survive. For this reason, moles are highly active mammals and have earned the reputation of being voracious predators. Apart from earthworms, a wide variety of other items may also be sampled, including beetles, cockchafers, slugs, millipedes and snails. Reports of moles catching and killing frogs, mice and even other moles most likely refer to their feeding on carrion, as such activity is not part of their normal behaviour.

A mole may obtain its food in several ways: either directly while constructing a tunnel, for example if it unearths an earthworm while digging, by regularly patrolling its existing tunnel system and harvesting any prey which it discovers; or, finally, by searching the surface. Most likely, a combination of all three is practised. Searching the surface for prey is often profitable during a rain shower which follows a particularly dry period, since many soil invertebrates will be attracted to the surface in order to feed and mate. Such an occasion may also lead a mole to discover carrion. Surface hunting is a normal activity for the desert-dwelling moles of the Namib Desert, as these animals feed on lizards which bask on the sand's surface. Feeding in this manner, however, exposes the animal to a much wider range of predators and the European mole is unlikely to use this technique unless there is considerable ground cover available.

Of these three feeding methods, the second, using the 'tunnel trap' system, appears to be the most profitable means of locating food. Once a potential item of prey has been detected — usually by scent — it will be seized between the front paws in a vice-like grip. At the same time, the mole's hind limbs will be spread to support the body, which will then be lowered to the ground. Once captured, prey items are rapidly dealt with: small prey such as grubs and earthworm cocoons are eaten in a straight-

19. *The seasonal variation in a mole's diet is a reflection of the availability of prey.*

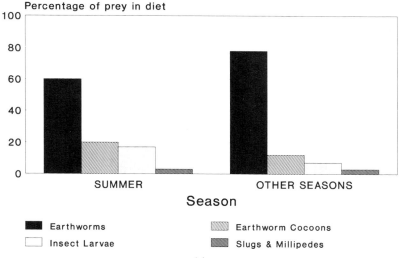

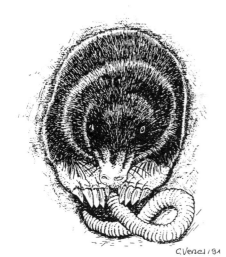

20. *Excess earth and grit are removed from earthworms by pulling them through the claws.*

forward manner, whereas earthworms present more of a challenge. These are first pinned down and manipulated by the forelimbs so that they are presented head first to the mouth. Earthworms are then quickly decapitated and gradually pulled between the claws of the forefeet with repeated upward jerking motions of the head. This serves to cleanse the outer skin of the worm and also squeezes out any remaining grit from the gizzard, since this would result in wearing down the mole's teeth, a common cause of death amongst older animals. Feeding is invariably followed with a grooming session and a short frantic search of the area for additional prey.

Like many mammals, moles are opportunistic feeders which, if they find themselves faced with a sudden abundance of prey, will take precautionary steps to store some of this in case it may be required later. This behaviour is known as food caching or hoarding and appears to be a well practised feature amongst certain animals, usually those which live in unstable environments where prey availability or climatic conditions are not always favourable. Thus not all moles will exhibit this behaviour, but research has now shown that certain moles will do so year after year. Those moles which do establish larders of prey are highly selective in the species which they choose, usually hoarding only large earthworms. This is most likely an energetic consideration since it would not be efficient for a mole to expend its energy storing very small prey. Earthworms discovered in these caches have been decapitated, which renders them immobile, and each has been individually sealed into a small crevice off a main chamber in the tunnel system. Stored prey is usually accumulated in just one or two places, often close to the nest site. The amount of time and work that a mole invests in this process is indicated by the author's discovery of a single cache which consisted of over 1500 earthworms! Such resources therefore represent a considerable effort on behalf of the resident mole, who must rely on them during periods of prey scarcity.

This same ability to adapt their behaviour to prevailing conditions is also evident in the diet of moles during the different seasons. During very dry or cold periods most soil invertebrates become immobile or retreat more deeply into the soil column, where they may find moisture and warmth. To compensate for a temporary shortage of prey near the surface, moles either follow the prey deeper into the soil, creating new, deeper tunnels in which to trap prey, or they switch their feeding behaviour to take whatever prey might be available. In fact, both reactions occur, which is why moles enlarge their tunnel systems as soon as it gets very cold or dry, and also why they feed on more insect larvae and earthworm cocoons during dry periods of the year.

Even though most of their prey is composed of fluids (over 60 per cent in the case of earthworms), moles still require a constant source of water and thus cannot survive in especially arid regions. For much of the year in the northern climate this does not pose any problem but, during periods of drought, moles may have to undertake what for them are lengthy excursions (1-2 km) in search of water. Moles have also been reported as coming to the surface early in the morning to lick the dew from the grass.

21. A cross-section of a fortress, showing the many galleries and layers of tunnels.

Few moles have direct access to a permanent source of water from their normal territory and therefore run the risk of meeting other moles and perhaps even having to cross the territories of neighbouring animals, which may also result in conflicts. In folklore, however, there are many references to 'communal mole tunnels' leading to water, and professional molecatchers also know that such runs exist and are particularly worth searching for. The mole's behaviour under such circumstances is still unclear and it is not known whether there are regular conflicts in such tunnels or whether the animals have a common, non-aggressive pact under such conditions.

This is another interesting example of the mole's navigational skills, as they are able to move considerable distances outside their normal territories without getting lost. Moles are also strong swimmers and, despite their poor eyesight, the author has seen a mole plunge into a stream and head determinedly to another tunnel entrance on the opposite bank, some 7 metres away! How they retain such an accurate visual plan of their tunnel systems remains a mystery.

Activity and behaviour

Considering the constant need for vigilance in this underground milieu, as well as the need to feed at regular intervals, moles are active during each 24 hour period. Unlike many other small mammals, European moles do not hibernate or even enter torpor when environmental conditions (temperature and prey availability) deteriorate. Instead they remain active throughout the year. One species of African golden mole (*Amblysomus hottentotus*), which lives in arid lands in southern Africa, does, however, appear to enter torpor as a means of saving body energy. This strategy enables the animals to withstand the harsh conditions of this region.

For much of the year the European mole displays a distinct triphasic pattern consisting of three phases of activity and of inactivity every 24 hours: periods of activity usually last from four to four and a half hours, during which time they forage and explore, alternating with similar periods of rest, which are spent in the nest. Sometimes, a period of intense activity — such as digging a new tunnel — may be interrupted by a sudden need or desire for a rest. Rather than return to the nest chamber, a mole may simply take a brief catnap wherever it happens to be in the tunnel system.

Longer periods of rest are, however, spent in the nest, where the animal may remain for periods of three to four hours. This time is devoted solely to resting, except for lactating females, which must also meet the needs of their offspring. Indeed, during the nursing period there is a noticeable increase in the time that females spend foraging, as the energetic demands of raising a family single-handed require a major investment, so that the mother must increase her hunting behaviour.

Each bout of activity is usually preceded by a period of grooming, followed by a few structural adjustments to the nest. Whenever active, moles are intent on locating prey, protecting their territory from poten-

tial competitors, or maintaining or enlarging the existing tunnel system. Such activities account for almost 55 per cent of each day. Of this amount, 49 per cent of the time is spent moving, 41 per cent digging and approximately 10 per cent dozing in the tunnels, away from the nest. These values will differ greatly according to season and the region: moles living in fertile, well cultivated soils will not need to invest as much energy either in tunnel construction or feeding as will, for example, animals living in less than ideal conditions, such as those on shallow stony ground or in coniferous forests. Likewise, during the breeding season, males will often forsake their own familiar tunnel systems and wander over considerable distances looking for females whom they will court. During this period males are unable to feed at their normal rates and therefore undergo a considerable weight loss (almost 30 per cent of their body weight).

In general, however, the activity patterns of individual moles are closely synchronised on a daily basis, with a slight shift in

22. *The gardener's bane: molehills at Hardwick Hall in Derbyshire.*

DAY

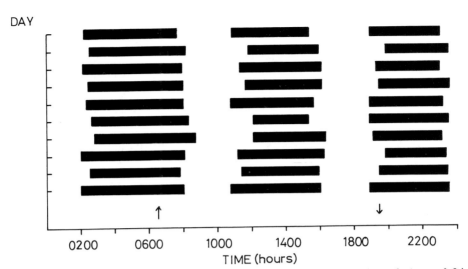

TIME (hours)

23. *A mole usually exhibits three distinct phases of sleep (dark bars) and activity during each 24 hour period. The onset of activity varies seasonally. Sunrise and sunset are indicated by arrows.*

timing as the year progresses. Moreover, within an established population, such as those in old permanent pastures, neighbouring animals display a strong tendency to synchronise their daily patterns of activity, that is, the timing of onset and cessation of activity is similar. Thus, within a particular area, all moles will either be active or at rest at a given time. Moles from a completely different population might display a slightly different pattern of activity. This suggests that moles are obtaining some common signal from their environment which initially triggers the onset of activity and which thereafter is regulated by an established pattern of social organisation.

Of the possible environmental factors, the onset of activity in the morning appears to be most closely correlated with sunrise. One reason for this may be that earthworms, which will have fed at the surface during the night, retreat into the soil before sunrise. In doing so, a number of these may fall into the cunningly laid tunnel trap,

24. *The daily activities of a mole are almost evenly divided between sleeping in its nest and exploring its tunnel system.*

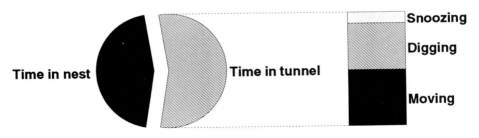

18

where they may be detected by the vigilant mole. Thus, by being active at this time, moles may optimise their prey catch rate. It is still unclear, however, if moles are able to detect such subtle changes in light intensity from deep within their tunnel systems.

BREEDING

Moles are essentially solitary and aggressive animals and it is only during the very brief breeding season that the animal's normal defensive barriers are lowered. The timing of the breeding season is controlled by environmental conditions: in Europe, for example, breeding amongst common moles may begin in February in Italy but will not commence in Scotland or Denmark until late March. For much of the year, the sex glands and reproductive tracts of both sexes are very small and show no signs of activity. However, with the onset of breeding, these glands rapidly mature.

The period during which females are in oestrus and receptive to the male is usually very short, probably only three or four days. Amongst moles, it is always the male which searches for a suitable female and this is the only time of the year when a female will tolerate another mole within her territory. Males are very cautious in their approach to females since they are generally highly aggressive if they are not ready to mate. It is likely that males are able to detect oestrus females by odour. There are few accounts of the mating behaviour of moles but these conclude that mating takes place at or near the female's nest, the male remaining with the female for a period of one to two hours. In order to maximise their opportunities of fathering a large number of offspring, males attempt to mate with as many females as possible. This is therefore a particularly frenetic time for males, who abandon their normal territories and undergo lengthy excursions in search of possible mates. Males do not participate in rearing the young.

Following a gestation period of four weeks, the mother will give birth to an average of four infants at the nest site. Newborn moles are pink and hairless and rely on their mother for warmth since they cannot control their own body temperatures very successfully at this age. Even at birth, the pronounced features of the body are the massive shoulders and forelimbs.

Weighing only 3.5 grams at birth, the young are fed entirely on the mother's rich milk for almost one month, during which time they rapidly gain weight. After about

25. *Mole body weight varies throughout the year: males are always heavier than females. Juveniles are usually born in May or June, depending upon local conditions.*

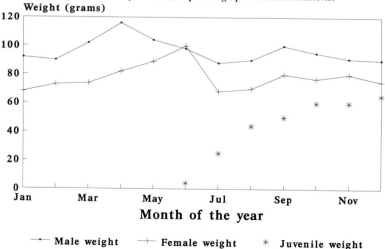

19

two weeks the fur begins to grow, and by three weeks they weigh about 40 grams and measure about 80 mm in length. The eyes usually open by the fourth week, by which stage the body is covered in a beautiful coat of shimmering silver-black fur.

By their fifth week, the juveniles will have started to explore their immediate surroundings and, together with their mother, will undertake brief forays outside the nest chamber. Two weeks later they will be actively exploring the maternal burrow system, searching for their own food. Juveniles usually remain with the mother for a further two weeks, gradually extending the range of their explorations until, finally, they will disperse from these burrows to establish their own tunnel systems. Those young that do not disperse of their own accord will eventually be forced to do so by the mother.

At nine weeks, now fully developed and only slightly smaller than an adult female, juveniles attempt to establish their own tunnel system. Dispersal takes place on the surface and it is during this period that most people might encounter a mole. At first, juveniles wander extensively and seemingly lack any knowledge of how to dig. Inadvertently, many will wander into tunnel systems already occupied by other animals, who will not delay in evicting the intruders, once detected.

The juvenile dispersal period is the most critical time in the life of a mole because of its vulnerability whilst exposed on the surface and also because it must rapidly learn to establish its own tunnel system. By remaining concealed under leaves or grass many will avoid detection by ever present predators. However, many will fail to establish their own tunnel system and die from heat loss and starvation.

Those animals that do succeed in creating their own tunnels — and a high proportion of those weaned will do so — will reach maturity and breed during the following spring. Depending upon environmental conditions and the species concerned, the number of litters and offspring produced varies: two litters per annum are common for the European mole in Italy and France, whereas further north, in Scotland and Denmark, only one litter will be produced. Because of the favourable climate and year-round availability of food, African species may breed throughout the year, with no fixed breeding period.

SOCIAL BEHAVIOUR

Moles are largely solitary and, with the exception of a brief respite during the breeding season, they are highly aggressive towards other moles of either sex. Each mole maintains its own tunnel network which it has either constructed itself or occupied following the emigration, death or eviction of the former owner. This defended area is known as its territory and in each case the resources within the tunnel network must be sufficient to support the daily requirements of the resident mole.

The size and shape of the territory depend on the sex of the resident, the habitat and the season. The territory of an adult male is always larger than that of a female and ranges from 3000 square metres during the summer to as much as 7000 square metres during the breeding season. In contrast, females' territories remain relatively constant at approximately 2000 square metres throughout the year. Poorer-quality habitats, such as moorlands, uplands or sand dunes, where prey density is low, result in larger territories than those found in deciduous woodlands and arable land, where prey density is higher.

Each mole visits most of its territory on a daily basis, thereby familiarising itself with its own tunnel system. The tunnels of neighbouring moles are often connected and, although the animals rarely meet, they are always aware if there is another mole nearby. Neighbouring moles avoid direct confrontation by foraging in the areas of overlap during different periods of activity.

The mechanism behind this apparently well controlled traffic system appears to be regulated by odour. Moles possess a large number of scent glands, the most important of which appear to be the paired preputial glands. Secretions are emitted from these glands, mixed with the urine and deposited throughout the animal's territory. Neck glands also produce secretions which are particularly obvious amongst breeding

13|

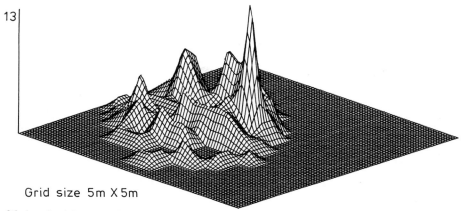

Grid size 5m X 5m

26. *A mole visits most of its territory during a 24 hour period, but shows a distinct preference for different parts of its range. In this graph, the highest peaks are the territorial boundaries of a neighbouring mole.*

males. There are distinctive chemical differences between the smell of a male and that of a female and it is likely that individual moles have their own subtle distinctive fragrance which will be readily distinguishable to other moles.

Whereas the core area of a mole's territory is rarely violated by other moles (as long as the resident is present), peripheral zones are heavily used and shared by neighbouring animals. Following the death or artificial removal of a mole from its territory, neighbouring moles will invade and often usurp this vacant space within 24 hours. However, if the general odour of a long-term resident is artificially maintained in that area, no incursions occur, confirming that as long as an animal regularly visits its territory scent will be deposited which will notify other moles that the area is already occupied. In this way unnecessary confrontations and potentially aggressive encounters are avoided.

POPULATION PARAMETERS

Moles are relatively long-lived compared to other mammals of similar size such as voles, mice or shrews. In the wild moles usually live for at least two years and in most stable populations there will be a few animals of five years of age. Within any population juveniles (less than one year old) are the most common cohort (45 per cent), followed by one- to two-year old animals (40 per cent) and two- to three-year olds (13 per cent). The remaining two per cent are over three years old. In any population the sexes are usually equally represented.

Tooth wear is one of the most common causes of death, with those animals that inhabit sandy or coarse gravel-type soils generally suffering most, as they will naturally ingest a considerable amount of grit when feeding. To avoid an intake of too much grit, the mole generally cleans the outside of its prey by pulling it through its claws (see above). If a mole is unable to construct its own tunnel system following dispersal or eviction from its previous territory it may suffer from starvation, particularly in cold weather, when soil invertebrates themselves will be rather inactive.

Good fur condition is essential at all times of the animal's life and a mole with poor fur will quickly succumb to death in cold or wet conditions. Constant grooming is therefore an essential prerequisite to maintaining good health, not only because it prevents the fur from becoming entangled, but also as it removes grit and excess moisture from the hair. Grooming is also important as it helps remove external parasites.

Little is known about the effect of parasites on moles, although anyone who has handled a live mole or even its nest will quickly be impressed at the number of ectoparasites that the animals carry. The most obvious parasites are different species of fleas, such as *Palaeopsylla minor*, which is the most commonly found species, *Ctenophthalmus nobilis* and *Hystrichopsylla talpae*. The fur mite *Labidophorus soricis* and the tick *Ixodes hexagonus* are also often present. None of these ectoparasites is host-specific and they are generally found on a wide range of British small mammals. Moles may acquire these 'visitors' while collecting nesting materials from the surface, or indirectly as a result of other small mammals using either the mole's tunnel or its nest, which occurs frequently.

Unlike shrews or voles, mole populations do not undergo seasonal or annual population fluctuations and numbers remain relatively stable through the year and, indeed, between years. The density of moles within a region varies considerably according to the quality of the habitat, the availability and abundance of prey items being the most important factors in determining the density. Deciduous woodlands and permanent pastures, both highly fertile zones, support a mean density of four and five moles per hectare respectively. By comparison, in areas which do not support such high densities of prey, such as young coniferous woodlands or moorlands, the density of moles may be as low as one animal per hectare.

Moles and man

AN ECONOMIC PROBLEM

There are three main reasons why fossorial species in general, and moles in particular, are considered as pests. First, they may be the cause of minor nuisance involving small economic loss — for example, when moles tunnel across lawns, bowling greens, golf courses or cricket greens, throwing up molehills as they dig. These are considered to be aesthetically unattractive or may simply be a nuisance. Second, and a somewhat more serious problem, the tunnels and earth heaps produced by moles often provide the means for invasion and colonisation by other species, both plants (weeds) and animals. These latter species may then prove to be far more destructive than the original inhabitants. Last, and of much greater economic importance, is the direct damage that moles may cause either by uprooting seedlings and depriving the rooting system of water and soil, by damaging farm machinery or by causing contamination of stored crops such as silage through the collection of earth from the molehills during the harvesting process.

For these reasons, the mole has not enjoyed a particularly favourable relationship with man. Indeed the European mole has been persecuted for centuries, initially because of its luxurious coat, which in the form of either a waistcoat or trousers, was once prized by the gentry. Considering that it took over one hundred good pelts to make both front sections of a waistcoat, it was perhaps fortunate, for the moles at least, that this material did not wear out too quickly. Active trade in moleskins continued until as recently as 1950, when there was still a thriving export market from Germany and England.

Man is still the greatest threat to moles as he pursues widescale control programmes

27. *The spatial organisation of a female mole (stippled area) and the territories of three neighbouring males. Note the areas of overlap between neighbouring territories. Nest sites are indicated by stars.*

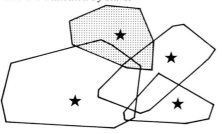

20m

against burrowing species, wherever they encroach on to his agricultural interests. The practice of mole control itself has undergone a steady change since the beginning of the twentieth century; from the once highly skilled professional art whereby a molecatcher would carefully set a single noose snare with a willow sapling for each animal, it has shifted to the semi-skilled laying of a wide array of modern traps and, more recently, to even less arduous techniques which involve the laying of poisoned baits or gas-releasing pellets.

Trapping is probably still one of the most effective and most humane methods of mole control. Present-day models such as the Duffus or 'half-barrel' traps are light and simple to use and have replaced the older, much more cumbersome harpoon-type traps. Even so, the use of traps requires skilled labour and is also extremely labour-intensive, since traps must be frequently revisited and, on occasion, reset. Today, however, mole control usually involves the use of poisonous compounds, such as strychnine or phosphine-generating pellets. Apart from humane considerations — failure to absorb the correct dosage means considerable suffering for the animal — the effectiveness and need for such control methods are still questioned and additional research is required to find alternative solutions to this problem.

Apart from man, moles have few natural predators, as one might expect for an animal which is well concealed below ground. The most dangerous period of the animal's life is during the dispersal phase (which takes place above ground), when moles are exposed to a wide range of predators and harsh environmental conditions. Major predators include buzzards, herons, foxes, weasels, owls, cats and dogs. Family pets often present their owners with moles, which have usually been captured on the surface. These will rarely be eaten by domestic animals because of the strong flavour emanating from the mole's numerous scent glands. However, in their natural empire below ground, moles have few enemies — the weasel being the only species that could pursue a mole through the labyrinthine network of tunnels.

STUDYING MOLES

Studying moles is a tedious and most frustrating hobby and few people who have ever attempted to venture into the field specifically to look for moles will have succeeded. At present the only feasible way of 'watching' these animals is first to catch them alive in specially constructed traps and then, with the aid of miniature radio transmitters attached to the body, follow them as they go about their daily activities below ground. In this manner one can amass a considerable amount of information on the behaviour and lifestyle of these fascinating but most secretive animals.

For most people this is not a realistic answer if they simply want to see a mole, as it is an expensive technique and, even still, requires a great deal of patience and perseverance. The author's first encounter with a mole — actually two animals — took place one day whilst ambling along a quiet country lane in northern Italy when a writhing, black, screaming ball erupted from the bank along a small track in some woodlands. Coming to rest near his feet, the object revealed itself to be two moles engaged in a furious battle, which continued for several minutes before one broke off and darted back into a concealed tunnel in the bank, being rapidly followed by the victor. Before that incident the author had never seen a mole. Since then, even after seven years of detailed research into these fascinating animals, he has seen only two moles wandering about on the surface!

Finding moles is therefore largely a matter of good fortune. Probably one of the best means of doing so is to wander about a freshly tilled field — taking care not to damage the crop — where one may frequently 'observe' a mole in the process of digging a tunnel. In such instances, a little patience may be rewarded by a head suddenly popping out of the tunnel. The temptation to dig the animal out for a quick look is quite strong in such cases but should be resisted as it often causes serious injury to the mole. Early morning is usually the best time to observe such activities. Those fortunate enough to glimpse a mole — perhaps a juvenile engaged in finding its new home — should not attempt to pick it up and should not be tempted to adopt it as a pet. Moles can be maintained quite successfully in captivity but require great attention and are much better left to explore their natural environment.

In recent years many species of moles have become threatened as a result of increased pressure for agricultural lands and the artificial manipulation of the environment. There is probably no immediate cause for concern about the future of the European mole, but it is likely that a number of local extinctions have already taken place as a result of human persecution. However, concern has rightly been expressed about many of the other members of this family. For example, aquatic species such as the fascinating desmans are particularly susceptible to changes in their habitat and it is feared that many populations have been destroyed in recent years as a result of drainage, construction of dams for hydro-electric power, excessive salting of mountain roads, destruction of riverine habitat and, because of their rarity and odd appearance, collecting as a novelty and for museums. The magnificent African giant golden mole (*Chrysospalax trevelyani*) is also severely threatened as a result of the destruction of its habitat — valley forests with deep soils.

Because of their small size, secretive nature and the somewhat destructive habits of some species, most people might not consider it a great loss if these animals were allowed to disappear. Some might even relish the thought. However, this must not be allowed to happen. It is vital that we appreciate that no single species should ever be viewed in isolation, but instead within the much wider context of the role that each occupies within the natural ecosystem. Ultimately, it is our responsibility to ensure that the tremendous natural diversity on Earth is preserved, to be enjoyed and appreciated by all. Therefore, as we continue to learn more about obscure animals such as moles and their intriguing relatives, we are gradually forming a better understanding of the natural ecosystem and of our own position within it. Such knowledge cannot be bought or rapidly acquired: it comes only as a result of patient observations — just like watching moles.

Further reading

Godfrey, G., and Crowcroft, P. *The Life of the Mole*. Museum Press, London, 1960.
Gorman, M. L., and Stone, R. D. *The Natural History of Moles*. Christopher Helm, London, 1990.
Mellanby, K. *The Mole*. New Naturalist 22, Collins, 1971.

ACKNOWLEDGEMENTS
I would like to dedicate this book to 'Cairn', a valued friend and trusty field companion. As always, thanks are due to Olga Sheean-Stone for her invaluable support. Corrine Versel provided the drawings, which greatly enhance the final product. Photographs were provided by: the Frank Lane Picture Agency, 1, 14 and 17 (Silvestris); Graham Hickman, 12, 15, 16 and 18; and Cadbury Lamb, 22. All other photographs are by the author.